A Special Edition of

The Mediterranean Refresh

Erika Simons

ISBN: 978-1-9995720-0-6

Table Of Contents

Welcome!

*T*hank you so much for getting this edition of my book, The Mediterranean Refresh. It's a complete introduction to the Mediterranean Diet and I'm sure you will love the recipes so much. Please feel free to grab more copies for your friends and family. Or simply tear pages out or take pictures of the recipes so you can share them.

My first goal with this book is to help you achieve your health goals. With the Mediterranean Diet, you can stabilize your weight and strengthen your heart health. But secondly, I want to introduce you to our community of people all with goals just like yours. I want you to flourish and I want to give you the support you need.

If you haven't already, feel free to join our community online! There you'll get access to our forum where I get together with thousands of others to swap recipes, share stories, and motivate each other. You'll also get access to free goodies including more recipes and lifestyle guides.

Visit your community at:
www.Peapil.com/Mediterranean

Introduction to the Mediterranean Lifestyle

I know... I know... It's called the Mediterranean Diet. But I hate that word... diet. It sounds like you're going to have to stop eating all your favorite foods. Start calorie counting. Join some cult-like exercise place. It's been used for decades to describe some pretty horrific things.

But – have no fear.

This book isn't about dieting, calorie counting, or anything like that. It's about adopting a lifestyle that's been around for hundreds of years. A lifestyle full of delicious, seasonal and fresh foods. The Mediterranean Diet is full of an unlimited amount of food from all food groups. Although there are different focuses that you may be unfamiliar with, no food groups are completely excluded. There are no hard and fast rules; just 'Less of this' and 'More of this' guidelines.

The diet is based on the eating habits of people on the coast of Italy, Morocco, Spain, Greece, and France. People living on the shores of the Mediterranean have a very healthy diet because of the abundance of heart-healthy foods found right outside their doors. Foods like fresh fish, nuts, and fruit. Imagine going to a Mediterranean vacation... you get to eat like this every day. Including... yes – a little bit of wine!

This isn't the typical restrictive North American "diet".

The Mediterranean Diet is widely acknowledged as one of the healthiest diets in the world. And for my money, when making a list of healthy and delicious diet, this is the best one in the world bar none.

People in the Mediterranean (that haven't already switched to a McDonald's heavy diet) ... have reduced risk of heart disease. The diet is associated with a lower level of oxidized low-density lipoprotein (LDL) cholesterol. This is the "bad" cholesterol that is likely to build up deposits in your arteries.

By eating the Mediterranean Diet, a study of nearly 26,000 women found that those who followed this type of diet had 25% less risk of developing cardiovascular disease over the course of 12 years.[1] This means they were less likely to die from heart-related diseases, and lived longer overall. Following the guidelines of a Mediterranean Diet resulted in lower levels of inflammation, blood sugar, and body mass index - all of which are the primary drivers of increased heart disease risks when their levels are too high. .

One myth that these studies have debunked is that by just eating "low-fat" foods you could reduce the risk of heart disease. As you'll discover, the Mediterranean Diet actually encourages eating fats - but good-for-you fats. That means lots of extra virgin olive oil and nuts. The risk of diabetes was also decreased by eating Mediterranean foods.[2]

Eating more olive oil and mixed nuts has also been shown to reduce breast cancer. The healthy fats you get from the Mediterranean Diet have also been linked to decreasing the likelihood of cancer, Parkinson's and even Alzheimer's. The same study also found that women who followed the Mediterranean Diet were 46% more likely to age healthfully.

Eating plants, whole grains, fish, and even a bit of red wine... plus skipping processed foods – it's a great way to get past 70 years old without developing chronic diseases or declines in mental health.[3]

Getting the fresh foods, healthy fats and natural sugars – as opposed to our typical processed, artificial, sugar-choked diet – leads to a longer, more productive life with less fear of mental and physical illnesses in the future.

The Mediterranean Diet has been recommended by the American Heart Association as a great way to try and prevent cardiac diseases.[4] And that's one of the primary reasons so many people turn to this lifestyle.

But the benefits of the Mediterranean Diet don't only happen as you age. You'll notice (and feel) some of the changes almost immediately.

Main Benefits of the Mediterranean Diet

- Detox the liver and colon
- Curb sugar cravings
- Boost energy levels
- Find and maintain ideal weight
- Fight inflammation
- Helps with heart health
- Makes blood sugar management easy

Why I Got Involved

My name is **Erika Simons** and I'm currently the head recipe coach over at **Mediterranean Refresh.** I joined the team there because it was created specifically for people like me and you to transform our bodies and lives.

I'm a mother and a daughter who has first-hand experience with the disastrous results of our processed, unnatural, sugar-filled lifestyles.

I wouldn't be the woman I am today if it wasn't for my mother. I owe her so much. I'm sure many of you can relate.

She was an incredible Chef who trained under some of the best culinary minds in California, and she taught me everything she knew about cooking. By the time I

was a teenager, she had taught me how to make authentic dishes from places like Japan, Italy, Greece, and so many others. The only trouble was, even though my Mom could create meals that people happily paid hundreds of dollars for, she struggled with her weight and more importantly, her health.

As a young girl, I watched her battle with an eating disorder.

While my family and I would eat the incredible dinners she cooked for us, she seemed only to push food around her plate with a fork, never taking a bite.

That was until I turned 14 and everything changed.

Her dietary habits were unsustainable, and her body didn't know what to make of the food she was eating.

This was the year my Mom was put into the hospital for the first time. She was never able to bring herself to eat the kinds of foods that would properly nourish her, and it took a severe toll on her health and our entire family.

So, for months at a time, we would visit her in the hospital.

Over the span of three years her health rapidly declined — until she passed away in May of 2003.

It was at this point, after the loss of my Mother, that I decided to take a stand and change my life.

This is all because of the standard American diet...

I decided I would never again eat anything that could threaten my chance to love my children for as long as possible. I was tired of being tired, overweight and headed down the same path as my mom.

So, from that point forward, healthy cooking became the key to unlocking my best possible life.

After reading about the problems caused by our typical diet, I became obsessed.

Surely, the longevity of a people indicated how good their overall diet is. So, I started researching different cultures. Which ones had the lowest rates of heart disease, Alzheimer's disease, Parkinson's disease. Where were people naturally lean and energetic?

During my hunt I discovered dozens of cultures with longer lives and less illness.

It was true: Our diets affect our lives more than we care to admit.

But... there was a problem.

So many of these 'healthy' diets were based on restrictive eating. Eating small amounts of bland, tasteless food. As a recipe developer, I consider delicious food as an essential part of life.

If you told me I'd live longer if I chose not to eat good food... I would tell you to get lost. A short life full of joy is better than a long one.

This is less extreme than that example... but it remains true. I NEED to eat delicious food. I'd rather die than eat bland, tasteless food all my life. It's just part of my soul.

That's when I stumbled on the Mediterranean Diet. My research indicated that it was in fact one of the best lifestyles in the world based on longevity and reduced incidents of diseases. And... when I explored the diet in more depth, I discovered just how delicious the food can be.

I decided to give it a shot.

I didn't have any recipes, and no idea how to get started.

But little by little, I started to feel a lot better.

I felt refreshed... energized! I was sleeping easier, and I had zero brain fog in the morning. After just a couple weeks....

I started spending more time with my children again. I was even more active at work!

It took months, but I eventually developed a whole catalogue of recipes to choose from. I started adapting my favorite American recipes to fit into the Mediterranean Diet. I adapted traditional Mediterranean recipes to make them easier to make. I only chose ingredients I could find at the local supermarket.

In time, I became really proficient as a Mediterranean chef, my friends and family started asking me for healthy recipes constantly. Every day, I see how the recipes I adapt and create are changing lives. My friends and family all have slimmer waistlines, higher energy, deeper sleep, and feel better overall.

...but friends and family kept asking me for the recipes. And after a while I got tired of constantly writing out each recipe.

So, I started looking into publishing at that's when I bumped into the Peapil Publishing team. They helped work with me and develop the wonderful recipes you see in this book today. All of these recipes are Mediterranean Approved and contain no artificial ingredients.

1. Ahmad S, Moorthy MV, Demler OV, Hu FB, Ridker PM, Chasman DI, Mora S. Assessment of Risk Factors and Biomarkers Associated With Risk of Cardiovascular Disease Among Women Consuming a Mediterranean Diet. JAMA Network Open. 2018

2. Salas-Salvadó J, Bulló M, Babio N, Martínez-González MÁ, Ibarrola-Jurado N, Basora J, Estruch R, Covas MI, Corella D, Arós F, Ruiz-Gutiérrez V. Reduction in the incidence of type 2 diabetes with the Mediterranean diet. Diabetes care. 2011

3. Samieri C, Sun Q, Townsend MK, Chiuve SE, Okereke OI, Willett WC, Stampfer M, Grodstein F. The Association Between Dietary Patterns at Midlife and Health in Aging: An Observational Study. Annals of internal medicine. 2013

4. Mediterranean Diet. www.heart.org. https://www.heart.org/en/healthy-living/healthy-eating/eat-smart/nutrition-basics/mediterranean-diet. Published 2019. Accessed January 14, 2019.

Essential Elements of The Mediterranean Diet

In a nut shell, the Mayo Clinic states this diet...

Emphasizes eating primarily plant-based foods, such as fruits and vegetables, whole grains, legumes and nuts. Replacing butter with healthy fats such as olive oil and canola oil. Using herbs and spices instead of salt to flavor foods.

The diet doesn't require eliminating fat from your diet. Many trending diets like Keto and Paleo recommend fat... and this diet is no different. It's overall a less restrictive diet that believes in fresh foods even whole grains and legumes.

1. Use Olive Oil

Olive oil is the primary source of fat in this diet. It provides monounsaturated fat – a type that reduces LDL (bad) cholesterol levels. We recommend "extra-virgin" because it has the highest levels of the plant compounds that actually provide antioxidant effects.

Recent research indicates that olive oil protects against developing chronic diseases and helps with diabetes, obesity and cancer. It has a cardioprotective role; providing a antihypertensive, antithrombotic, antioxidant, anti inflammatory and anti carcinogenic action.[2]

The diet isn't about limited total fat consumption, but rather making good choices about which fats to consume. To fully feel the effects of this dietary lifestyle, avoid saturated fats and hydrogenated oils which have trans fats. These unhealthy fats are tied to heart disease and will counteract all of the healing that your body is undergoing.

2. Eat Lots of Fish!

Don't worry – even if you're not a fish lover, there's plenty of delicious recipes to experiment with. Fish are rich sources of heart healthy omega-3 fatty acids.

The fish is cooked fresh and is never deep-fried. Don't worry, there are plenty of directions in the recipe section of this book.

3. Wine Time

The health effects of wine have been debated forever. But most experts agree that as long as you don't drink excessively, wine can be a wonderful component to your diet. If you choose to drink wine, we recommend limiting your consumption to 5 ounces per day for those over 65 and 10 ounces per day for those under 65.

4. Go Nuts

"[Nuts] contain the beneficial linolenic acid (a type of omega-3 fatty acid). Omega-3 fatty acids lower triglycerides, decrease blood clotting, are associated with decreased sudden heart attack, improve the health of your blood vessels, and help moderate blood pressure."

Nuts are another vital food group in the diet. Nuts are high in fat but most of the fat is not saturated. Make sure not to eat too much, about a handful a day. And avoid the corner store candied nuts. I recommend unsalted nuts and love fresh walnuts, acorns and almonds. Cashews are also amazing.

Replacing your regular snacks for nuts is a great way to reduce empty calories, added sugar and sodium. Nuts are also a great source of fiber and minerals like potassium. Much better than processed snack foods.

5. Eat Veggies and Fruit

Make sure to always include a handful of veggies or fruit in every dish you prepare. Don't be afraid to eat a piece of fruit or add it to a recipe for an extra bit of natural sweetness. In general, use fruit instead of adding sugar. One of the best parts of this diet is hitting up the local Farmer's Markets and choosing what to eat based on the seasons. It's a wonderful way to educate my children and they love going!

Rule of thumb: Eat veggies all day long... for every meal. It's simply the best way to get extra nutrients, fill your tummy without a ton of calories and it actually is proven to reduce stress.

Fruits are the best way to satisfy your sweet tooth. Because the sugar is naturally occurring and the fruit has fiber, it won't spike your blood sugar nearly as bad as the same amount of added sugar. Full of vitamin C and antioxidants, this is just a great way to complete a well-balanced diet.

6. Switch to Whole Grains

This is such a simple way to increase fiber and nutrition in your diet. I always recommend whole grains for a delicious guilt-free pasta dish.

Grains in the Mediterranean region are typically whole grain and contain very little trans fats. Bread is important to the diet but is never eaten with butter or margarines which we avoid because they contain trans fats.

7. Choose Olive Oil and Skip Butter

Olive oil makes a wonderful alternative to butter. We also have a wonderful tahini you can use as a dip or spread. Butter is not necessarily bad for you but compared to olive oil it has more saturated fats and less mono-unsaturated fat.

8. Less Red Meat

Substitute fish and poultry for red meat. When you do choose red meat, try to make the portions small. And always opt for fresh meat over preserved or processed meats like sausage and jerky.

9. Low-fat, No-Sugar Dairy

We recommend low-fat yogurt with no added sugar. It's an easy way to get all the benefits of dairy without the baggage.

10. Add Spices

Spices are full of nutrients and anti-inflammatory properties. Not to mention they can make any dish 10x more delicious. When going through the recipes, take note of which spices and herbs we recommend. Try to get good at knowing how much you like to add, and which ones are your favorite. Try to reduce the amount of added sugar you need to improve the recipes.

Living Better with the Mediterranean Diet

The Mediterranean Diet can help you achieve your weight goals or keep a stable, healthy weight. However, the strongest benefit of the diet is its ability to help avoid heart disease.

Tips for Success

Before you get started on the diet, it's good to do a little bit of preparation. Often times we jump right into things... and it's easy to get overwhelmed. So, read on a bit and study this before jumping into the recipes (unless you just need something fun to eat, then feel free to pick a recipe and get started!).

Adapt Your Current Diet

Before jumping into the diet completely, just take a look at what you currently eat and try and make subtle changes. Reduce the red meat, change the oil to olive oil. Try to do low fat yogurt. Reduce the number of sugary treats. Try to morph your current diet into the Mediterranean Diet instead of starting from scratch. Slowly moving towards this diet will make it harder to move back to your old ways.

Learn to make some simple substitutions. Instead of eating a bag of chips, grab a fistful of nuts. Find something in the Mediterranean Diet that will make a healthy replacement for all your current eating habits.

I've included a whole section on Snack foods, Drinks, and even Desserts to help keep you on track. Take a look at that section right now and think about which recipes there would be a great substitute for your current habits.

Your New Food Pyramid

Mediterranean Diet Pyramid: a lifestyle for today
Guidelines for Adult population

Serving size based on frugal
and local hab

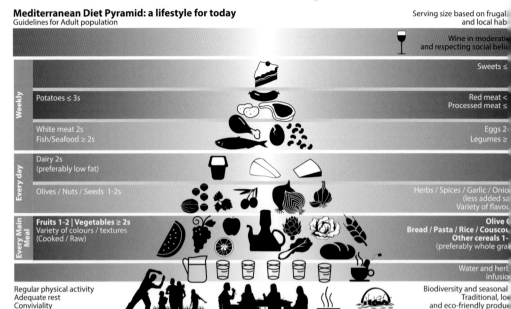

Wine in moderatic
and respecting social beli

Sweets ≤

Weekly

Potatoes ≤ 3s

Red meat <
Processed meat ≤

White meat 2s
Fish/Seafood ≥ 2s

Eggs 2-
Legumes ≥

Every day

Dairy 2s
(preferably low fat)

Olives / Nuts / Seeds 1-2s

Herbs / Spices / Garlic / Onio
(less added sa
Variety of flavou

Every Main Meal

Fruits 1-2 | Vegetables ≥ 2s
Variety of colours / textures
(Cooked / Raw)

Olive (
Bread / Pasta / Rice / Couscou
Other cereals 1-
(preferably whole gra

Water and herb
infusio

Regular physical activity
Adequate rest
Conviviality

Biodiversity and seasonal
Traditional, loc
and eco-friendly produc
Culinary activit

2010 edition

s = Serv

ICAF
International Commission on the
Anthropology of Food and Nutrition

Ciiscam

H.H.F.

Fundación
Dieta Mediterránea

FORUM ON
MEDITERRANEAN
FOOD CULTURES

Predimed
Prevención con Dieta Mediterránea

IUNS

CIHEAM
International Centre for Advanced
Mediterranean Agronomic Studies

fer

This food pyramid was developed by The Mediterranean Diet Foundation Expert Group and shows what foods you should eat as part of the diet. Each recipe in this book closely follows this pyramid.

Here's an example of a day with the Mediterranean Food Pyramid:

- *Fruits and Vegetables: 4+ servings*

Try to opt for fresh, seasonal fruits and veggies. If you're ever hungry, just know you can eat more veggies!

- *Heart Healthy Fats: 4-6 servings*
- *Whole Grains: 3-5 servings*
- *Seafood: 1 serving*

- *Dairy: 1 serving*
- *Red Wine: 5 ounces*
- *Meats: 1-2 servings*

Always opt for poultry over red meat, but still only eat small serving sizes.

The Pantry

In order to maintain the diet, it's important to stock up on some common ingredients that most of these recipes will share. That way you're not running to the grocery store every day! I made sure each recipe in this book uses common ingredients, so you're not running to specialty shops to try and find an obscure ingredient for a single recipe. No special equipment or appliances are needed.

Don't leave temptations in sight! Everything you buy at the grocery store will end up in your belly... so just leave the bag of chips there. It's so much harder to avoid indulgence when the food is right there... waiting to be eaten. How often have you heard yourself say, "I wouldn't eat this, but it's going to go bad... so I have to!"? It happens so often to me... Best to just cut out the temptation now.

Take a good look at your pantry and fridge. With the directions, I gave you earlier in this book try to give away or toss out some unhealthy ingredients. I know it can be hard and seems like a big waste of money. But the benefits of making a clean switch to this healthier way of living is way more valuable than the unhealthy food you need to get rid of.

This includes getting rid of your less healthy oils and margarine. Make sure to stock up on lots of great olive oil.

Enjoy the Vacation

Take your time. Remember when I said the Mediterranean Diet is like eating as if you're on vacation? One of the core tenants of the diet is to take things slowly when eating. Instead of shoving food down as quick as possible after going through a drive-thru or mindlessly eating while paying attention to Netflix, we invite you to sit down at the table with your family and friends. Slowly enjoy and savor what you're eating.

Gathering with friends and family and enjoying a freshly made meal is a vital part of the Mediterranean culture. Even without friends, enjoying a meal with your loved ones – talking about the day and enjoying each other's presence... it's so amazing.

Not only with you enjoy the food better, eating slowly allows you to pay attention to your stomach. It's good to get an awareness of when you're truly full to prevent over eating. Taking smaller portion sizes is the easiest way to reduce weight.

Be prepared to stop eating when you're satisfied... so often we end up eating until we need to start undoing our belts! Really pay attention while you eat slowly, take notes on what changes you'd like to make to the food.

Argh... Exercise

No lifestyle book is complete without a little blurb about exercise. Thankfully, if you go to our online community, you'll find dozens of resources that will help people just like yourself get into a more active lifestyle. I invite you to visit that community today!

www.Peapil.com/MediteranneanRefresh

Try to get about 20 minutes of exercise every day. It can be as simple as walking.

One "cheat" I use is to always take the stairs. I also make sure to park far away from the entrance when I go to the grocery store. Little things like this force you to get a bit of exercise in. I've also tried to get more involved with my daughter's activities. Instead of sending her to dance class, I actually joined a Mom/Daughter class so we can dance together! It's so much more fun than just watching her dance, I get to learn with her... and get some exercise!

How to Eat Out

When eating out, take care to pick a place where you're sure to get fresh and not fried food. If you do happen to slip-up and get fast-food, don't beat yourself up. Even being a full-time recipe developer... I sometimes end up with a sloppy burger in my hands! It's not going to kill you... just make sure it doesn't ruin your trend.

Lean more towards seafood places, farm-to-table restaurants or Italian, Spanish, and Greek restaurants. Vegetarian restaurants are also a great choice! That said, most restaurants have plenty of Mediterranean-style choices.

Avoid anything fried, and make sure to ask if you're not sure. Choose from the poultry or vegetarian options. Beef dishes are typically the most calorie laden. Be very careful with sauces and dressings - I typically ask for mine on the side. Try to avoid creamy sauces and ask for vinaigrette instead.

Most restaurants are used to substitutions do to allergies and dietary restrictions, so don't be afraid to tell them what you're unable to eat.

For example, ask to substitute regular tomato sauce for that alfredo you're about to order. Make sure to ask for extra veggies!

Side dishes are an easy place to slip up... but it's also an easy to place to make huge improvements. Instead of fries, upgrade to that salad. Drinks are also an easy place to make a mistake. A glass of red wine or sparkling water is a great alternative to sugary sodas and beer.

Don't be afraid to pack up your food for later. In fact, you should almost never finish a full meal at a restaurant. Restaurants are designed to make people satisfied... no matter their appetite. Especially if you're a smaller bodied person. Think about me for a second. I'm not a very tall woman... but the restaurant will serve the meal in the same size as my 6-foot tall husband!

I recommend skipping dessert for the most part. Unless they have a fruit bowl, opt for a tea or coffee. If skipping just isn't an option... make sure to split the dish with your partner.

Some Advice on Being Successful & What to Eat

The reason I turned to the Mediterranean Diet isn't just because it's extremely healthy... many diets are. But unlike most diets, I believe this one is full of foods you will enjoy. There's a wonderful variety of foods with very few forbidden choices. Really, it's just a shift in the amount you eat. There's no need to count calories if you eat properly and stop when you're satisfied.

Within just a few days, you'll be looking forward to your meals. Not just for the taste, but also for the feeling you get after you're finished eating good food. Feeling refreshed, not bloated. Satisfied, not stuffed. Energetic, not sluggish. You'll sleep better, have less brain fog... and rest easy knowing you're contributing to a healthy heart and brain.

The Mediterranean Diet is based in large part on eating a hearty amount of fresh produce including fruits and vegetables. Whole grains are eaten at most meals along with seafood several times a week. Meat is only in small portions, and not terribly often either.

Substitute olive oil for all your oils and butters. Try to avoid all creamy sauces and dressings. opt for vinaigrettes and tomato-based sauces. Clear soups are also great! But avoid chunky, sodium filled soups.

Shopping Guide

Every ingredient in this book can be sourced at your local grocery store. But I definitely recommend exploring your local shops. Find the best fish monger to go to. Check out your favorite butcher. And make sure to pick up seasonal fruits and veggies from your farmer's market. Bread should come from your local bakery, if they serve whole-wheat. Make sure to talk to these people, they're often highly knowledgeable about food and will make recommendations based on your diet and aspirations.

I highly recommend making ingredient substitutions based on what you can find locally! When shopping at the grocery store, stay away from prepackaged foods. Try to stick to the fresh food aisles. The freezer section can be handy for grabbing fuits and veggies that are currently out of season.

It may be difficult at first to figure out your shopping routine but begin to take note of where ingredients are kept, and you'll make your shopping trip quickly in no time.

Thank You!

Before I let you dive into the recipes, I just want to thank you for picking up and reading this book. It means so much to me that you've decided to incorporate my recipes into your life.

Enjoy! And I can't wait to see you in the community.

Erika Simons

1. Mediterranean Diet. www.heart.org. https://www.heart.org/en/healthy-living/healthy-eating/eat-smart/nutrition-basics/mediterranean-diet. Published 2019. Accessed January 14, 2019.

2. CA B. The role of olive oil in disease prevention: a focus on the recent epidemiological evidence from cohort studies and dietary intervention trials. - PubMed - NCBI. Ncbi.nlm.nih.gov. https://www.ncbi.nlm.nih.gov/pubmed/26148926. Published 2019. Accessed January 14, 2019.

Mediterranean

Breakfast

Breakfast

Cherry Whole-Wheat Pancakes

YIELD: *2 Servings*

ACTIVE TIME: *10 Min*

TOTAL TIME: *25 Min*

Ingredients

Pancakes
½ cup of whole-wheat flour
¼ cup quick oats
Pinch of salt
1 teaspoon baking powder
½ teaspoon cinnamon
1 small egg
½ cup of almond milk
¼ cup honey
2 tablespoons of Greek yogurt
½ teaspoon vanilla extract
¼ cup of cherries

Cherry Syrup
1 cup cherries, pitted and halved
1 cup water
1 cup honey

Directions

To start with the syrup, bring cherries, water, and honey to a boil. Simmer for 2 minutes. Strain the syrup and press the cherries so only the skin remains in the strainer. Place in a serving jar. Keeps in refrigerator for up to a month.

Now the pancakes! Toss the flour, oats, salt, baking powder, and cinnamon. In a different bowl whisk the egg and milk, then add the honey, yogurt, and vanilla until smooth. Pour the wet ingredients into the first bowl with the flour. Gently mix (do not overmix or the pancakes will be too tough). Now you can cook the pancakes in a frying pan, just add a dash of olive oil so they don't stick.

Serve hot with halved cherries and the syrup!

Oatmeal Banana Chips and Walnuts

2

YIELD *1 Serving* | **ACTIVE TIME** *5 Min* | **TOTAL TIME** *15 Min*

Ingredients

1 13.5 oz can coconut milk, unsweetened

1 cup old fashioned oats

3 tablespoons maple syrup

¼ cup banana chips (or fresh banana)

¼ cup walnuts (or almonds)

1 tablespoon flax seeds (or chia seeds)

1 tablespoon almond butter

Directions

Bring coconut milk to a boil then reduce heat to medium. Add in oats and cook for about 5 minutes, stirring frequently until soft and the milk is absorbed. Stir in maple syrup to taste. Top with banana chips, walnuts, flax seeds, and a dab of almond butter.

3 Fresh Banana and Power Seed Porridge

YIELD *1 Serving* | **ACTIVE TIME** *5 Min* | **TOTAL TIME** *15 Min*

Ingredients

½ cup porridge oats

1 cup milk

Pinch of salt

¼ cup banana, sliced

1 tablespoon chia seeds

1 tablespoon flax seeds

1 teaspoon turmeric

Directions

Combine the oats and milk in a saucepan with a pinch of salt. Bring to a boil and simmer over low heat for 5 minutes. Pour into a serving bowl and top with banana, chia seeds, flax seeds, and tumeric.

4 *Banana Toast*

YIELD *1 Serving* | **ACTIVE TIME** *5 Min* | **TOTAL TIME** *5 Min*

Ingredients

1 slice of whole-wheat bread

1 tablespoon almond butter

¼ cup banana, sliced

1 tablespoon dark chocolate chips

1 tablespoon sesame seeds

1 Strawberry (optional)

Directions

Toast the bread in a toaster or oven. Spread almond butter and top with banana slices, chocolate chips, and sesame seeds. Serve with a strawberry, yogurt dish or fruit for a filling breakfast.

Avocado and Spinach Toast

YIELD *1 Serving* | **ACTIVE TIME** *5 Min* | **TOTAL TIME** *15 Min*

Ingredients

2 slices whole-wheat bread

1 avocado

1 teaspoon lime juice

Pinch of Salt

1 cup spinach

1 Egg (optional)

Directions

Enjoy the bread fresh or toasted. Mash up avocado in a bowl with the lime juice and salt. Spread the avocado mixture on the toast and top with fresh spinach. For more food, feel free to top with a poached or sunny-side up egg.

6 Mediterranean Breakfast Bowl

YIELD *1 Serving* | **ACTIVE TIME** *5 Min* | **TOTAL TIME** *15 Min*

Ingredients

5 tablespoons oats

½ cup water

1 cup Greek yogurt

¼ cup raspberries, mashed

¼ cup strawberries, mashed

6 black raspberries (or blackberries)

1 tablespoon granola

Mint, chopped

1 tablespoon honey

Directions

In a saucepan, bring water to a bowl and add in oats. Simmer for 3 minutes over low heat, until oats are soft. Once cooked, spoon oatmeal into a serving bowl. Stir in yogurt, raspberries and strawberries. Top oatmeal mixture with black raspberries, granola, mint, and a drizzle of honey.

7 Egg Muffin

YIELD *3 Servings* | **ACTIVE TIME** *5 MINS* | **TOTAL TIME** *20 MINS*

Ingredients

2 tablespoons olive oil

3 eggs

2 tablespoons milk

2 tablespoons parmesan cheese

8 grape tomatoes, sliced

1 cup kale, chopped

Salt and pepper to taste

Directions

Preheat oven to 375F. Lightly brush a 6-cup muffin tray with olive oil. In a bowl, whisk the eggs, milk, and cheese. Pour egg mixture into the muffin tray. Mix all the veggies together and add them in equal parts to each muffin cup. Bake in the center of the oven for about 15-20 minutes or until toothpick can be removed cleanly.

Serve with a slice of whole-wheat toast.

Mediterranean

~ Lunch ~

Lunch

Mediterranean Salad Dressing

YIELD *3 Cups* | **ACTIVE TIME** *10 Min* | **TOTAL TIME** *3 Hours 10 Minutes*

Ingredients

¾ cup red wine vinegar

½ tablespoon oregano

½ tablespoon basil

2 teaspoons salt

1 tablespoon onion powder

1 garlic clove, minced

1 ½ tablespoons Dijon mustard

1 teaspoon black pepper

1 ½ cups olive oil

Directions

Combine red wine vinegar, oregano, basil, salt, onion powder, garlic, mustard, and black pepper in a blender. Blend while slowly incorporating the olive oil, until well combined. Transfer to a jar or container and chill, about 3 hours. Shake before serving. Adjust herbs, salt and pepper to your individual preference.

② Pear Power Salad

YIELD *1 Serving*	**ACTIVE TIME** *10 Min*	**TOTAL TIME** *10 Min*

Ingredients

1 pear, sliced

¼ cup walnuts, chopped

¼ cup blue cheese

¼ cup grapes

1 ½ cups baby greens (or mesclun)

*3 tablespoons **Mediterranean Salad Dressing***

Directions

In a bowl, combine pear slices, walnuts, blue cheese, grapes, baby greens. Toss with **Mediterranean Salad Dressing.**

3 Sunny Beet Salad

YIELD *1 Serving* | **ACTIVE TIME** *20 Min* | **TOTAL TIME** *90 Min*

Ingredients

1 small beet

1 tablespoon olive oil

1 orange, peeled and chopped

1 ½ cups arugula

¼ cup crushed walnuts

*3 tablespoons **Mediterranean Salad Dressing***

Directions

Preheat oven to 425F. Coat beet with olive oil and wrap in foil. Place in oven and roast until fork-tender (about 1 hour). Let cool for 10 minutes. Remove skin and slice the beet. In a bowl, toss beet slices, orange, arugula, walnuts, and the Mediterranean Salad Dressing. Feel free to add additional nuts or top with your favorite cheeses.

4 Cheesy Chard Salad

YIELD *1 Serving* | **ACTIVE TIME** *5 Min* | **TOTAL TIME** *5 Min*

Ingredients

1 cup chard

¼ cup grape tomatoes, halved

¼ cup soft cheese (or feta)

½ cup red onion, sliced

*2 tablespoons **Mediterranean Salad Dressing***

Directions

Combine all ingredients in a bowl and toss. Enjoy a deliciously simple salad!

5 Open Tuna Sandwich

YIELD *6 Servings* | **ACTIVE TIME** *5 Min* | **TOTAL TIME** *5 Min*

Ingredients

1 whole-wheat baguette

2 tins of tuna chunks

3 green onion stalks

¼ cup low-fat cream cheese

Salt and pepper

1 tablespoon olive oil (optional)

Directions

Cut the baguette into 6 half-inch slices and spread with cream cheese. Add the chunks of tuna and garnish with green onions. Sprinkle with salt and pepper. Drizzle with olive oil for added flavor and healthy fat.

6 Tuna Pita Pockets

YIELD *2 Servings* | **ACTIVE TIME** *5 Min* | **TOTAL TIME** *5 Min*

Ingredients

1 can solid tuna in water, drained

1 teaspoon lemon juice

1 cup lettuce

½ cup bell pepper, diced

¼ cup cucumber, sliced

1 whole-wheat pita pocket, halved

2 teaspoons Dijon mustard

¼ cup Greek yogurt

Directions

In a mixing bowl, combine the tuna, lemon juice, lettuce, red pepper and cucumber. Open the pita pockets with care to not rip them. Mix mustard and yogurt. Spread sauce on one side of the pita. Stuff pita with salad mixture.

7 Tuna Salad

YIELD *1 Serving* | **ACTIVE TIME** *10 Min* | **TOTAL TIME** *10 Min*

Ingredients

½ tin solid tuna chunks in water, drained

2 tablespoons red onion, diced

¼ teaspoon Dijon mustard

1 tablespoon Greek yogurt

2 cups spring mix lettuce

¼ cup grape tomatoes, halved

¼ cup bell pepper, sliced

*2 tablespoons **Mediterranean Salad Dressing***

Directions

Combine tuna, onion, mustard, and yogurt together to make the tuna salad. Set aside. Rip the lettuce into small pieces and layer on a plate. Top with tomatoes and bell pepper. Top salad with tuna mixture and drizzle with Mediterranean salad dressing.

Mediterranean
Dinner

Dinner

One Pan Mediterranean Chicken

YIELD *4 Servings* | **ACTIVE TIME** *25 Min* | **TOTAL TIME** *25 Min*

One Pan Mediterranean Chicken can be a nutritious, protein and vegetable filled healthy choice for dinner. Garnished with fresh herbs, it can be presented on the dinner table within thirty minutes.

Ingredients

1 ⅓ tablespoons olive oil

1 ½ pounds chicken breast

1 small white onion, sliced

1 clove garlic, sliced

1 tablespoon fresh oregano

½ cup green olives

½ cup bell pepper, diced

7.5 oz. can diced tomatoes

1 tablespoon fresh basil

¼ teaspoon black pepper

Salt, to taste

Directions

Heat one tablespoon of olive oil in a large frying pan over medium heat. When the oil is heated, add the chicken. Cook until golden brown in color and cooked through, about 10 minutes. Set aside chicken.

Pour remaining olive oil in the pan and add onion. Cook for two minutes and add sliced garlic for one more minute, until fragrant. Add oregano, olives, and red pepper. Keep cooking for 7-8 minutes more until peppers are soft.

Add diced tomatoes and cooked chicken, and bring to temperature.

Serve warm with potatoes or brown rice.

2 Mediterranean Salmon

YIELD: *2 Servings*

ACTIVE TIME: *10 Minutes*

TOTAL TIME: *25 Minutes*

Ingredients

1 tablespoon parsley

½ cup sundried tomatoes

¼ cup feta cheese, crumbled

¼ cup olives, chopped

1 tablespoon balsamic vinegar

1 tablespoon olive oil

Black pepper and salt, to taste

2 salmon fillets

Directions

Heat oven to 350F.

To prepare feta-olive tapenade: Mix parsley, sundried tomatoes, feta, olives, balsamic vinegar, and olive oil. Sprinkle black pepper and salt to taste. Set aside.

Rinse salmon thoroughly with cold water and then remove skin carefully. Sprinkle salmon with salt and pepper. Pour a few spoons of water in the baking dish and place salmon on it (to save from drying). Bake in preheated oven for 15 minutes until light pink and flaky. Lightly drizzle cooked salmon with lemon juice and brush with feta-olive tapenade

Mediterranean Olive Pasta

3

YIELD *4-6 Servings* | **ACTIVE TIME** *14 Min* | **TOTAL TIME** *20 Min*

Ingredients

6 oz. whole-wheat spaghetti

3 tablespoons olive oil

4 cloves garlic

2 cups cherry tomatoes

1 tin anchovies

1 cup olives, sliced

½ teaspoon red pepper flakes

¼ cup lemon juice

½ teaspoon black pepper

¼ cup parmesan cheese, grated

¼ cup parsley

Directions

Bring a large pot of water to a boil. Add in spaghetti and cook until al-dente, about 8-10 minutes. Drain pasta and set aside.

Meanwhile, combine olive oil, garlic, cherry tomatoes, anchovies, and olives in a pan over medium heat. Cook until fragrant. Stir in red pepper flakes, lemon juice, and black pepper. Mix in cooked pasta. Serve topped with parmesan and parsley.

4 Gluten Free Baked Falafel (Vegan option, Tzatziki Dressing)

YIELD *12 Servings* | **ACTIVE TIME** *30 Min* | **TOTAL TIME** *45 Min*

MAIN DISH: *Vegan, Vegetarian, Gluten free*

Ingredients

Salad

2 cups spring mix lettuce

½ cup olives

1 cucumber, sliced

1 cup cherry tomatoes, halved

1 red onion, sliced

Falafel

1 15 oz. can chickpeas, rinsed and drained

¼ cup oat flour

2 cloves garlic

1 red onion, chopped

½ cup parsley

½ cup cilantro

2 tablespoons lemon juice

1 teaspoon cumin

½ teaspoon salt

Ingredients

Tzatziki Dressing

1 cup Greek yogurt:

2 tablespoons dill

¼ cup cucumber, diced

1 tablespoon olive oil

1 tablespoon lemon juice

Black pepper and salt to taste

Directions

Set the oven temperature to 380F.

In a food processor, combine chickpeas, oat flour, garlic, onion, parsley, cilantro, lemon juice, cumin, and salt. Blend until ingredients form a thick, sticky batter.

Form batter into 1-inch patties on a lined baking tray.

Bake for 14-15 minutes. Flip and bake for 10-12 minutes more, until outside of patty is browned and inside is no longer sticky.

In a blender or food processor, combine yogurt, dill, cucumber, olive oil, lemon juice, black pepper, and salt. Blend until smooth.

Combine spring mix, olives, cucumber, tomatoes, and red onion. Top with falafel and drizzle tzatziki on top.

Tomato Mediterranean Pizza with Mozzarella

5

YIELD *3-5 Servings* | **ACTIVE TIME** *10 Min* | **TOTAL TIME** *20 Min*

Ingredients

1 teaspoon garlic, minced

1 red onion, chopped

1 cup mushroom, sliced

Pizza dough

1 8-10 oz, can pizza sauce

1 teaspoon oregano

1 teaspoon basil

1 cup mozzarella cheese

¼ cup feta cheese

Directions

Preheat oven to 450F. Over medium heat, sauté garlic and red onions for 2-3 minutes, until aromatic. Add mushrooms and cook until soft. Meanwhile, knead the dough into a twelve-inch discs. Bake dough on a lined tray or pizze stone for 3-5 minutes, until no longer sticky. Remove dough from oven and top with pizza sauce, oregano, and basil. Top with cheeses.

Bring the temperature down to 425F and bake for 10-12 minutes, until cheese is melted and crust is lightly browned.

6 Creamy Mediterranean Panini

YIELD *4 Servings* | **ACTIVE TIME** *20 Min* | **TOTAL TIME** *25 Min*

Ingredients

¼ cup mayonnaise

¼ cup basil leaves, chopped

2 tablespoons olives, sliced

8 slices whole-grain bread,

1 small zucchini, sliced

4 slices provolone cheese

1 cup roasted red bell peppers, sliced

8 slices bacon, cooked

2 tablespoons olive oil

Directions

Preheat panini press or grill pan. Combine mayonnaise with basil and olives in small bowl. Spread mayonnaise mixture evenly on 4 of the bread slices. Top these slices with zucchini, provolone, peppers and bacon. Close the sandwich with the other slice of bread. Lightly brush the outside of the sandwich with olive oil and cook until golden brown and cheese is melted, about 3 minutes.

⑦ Skillet Chicken with Olives

YIELD *4 Servings* | **ACTIVE TIME** *10 Min* | **TOTAL TIME** *30 Min*

Ingredients

4 boneless skinless chicken thighs

1 teaspoon rosemary

½ teaspoon black pepper

¼ teaspoon salt

1 tablespoon olive oil

½ cup olives

¼ cup white wine (or chicken broth)

1 tablespoon capers, drained (optional)

Directions

Sprinkle chicken with rosemary, pepper and salt. Heat oil in a large skillet over medium-high heat. Brown chicken on both sides. Add olives, wine, and capers.

Reduce heat to low, cover and simmer for 2-3 minutes.

Mediterranean

~ Drinks ~

Drinks

Sun Smoothie

YIELD *1 Drink* | **ACTIVE TIME** *3 Min* | **TOTAL TIME** *3 Min*

Ingredients

1 cup of almond milk

½ cup orange juice

¼ cup of wheat germ

1 banana, frozen

Directions

This vitamin boosting smoothie is perfect for a hot afternoon... the best part? It's incredibly easy to make. Place all four ingredients in a blender. Blend on high until smooth.

② Frosty Fruit Smoothie

YIELD *1 Drink* | **ACTIVE TIME** *5 Min* | **TOTAL TIME** *5 Min*

Ingredients

1 banana, frozen

1 cup strawberries

1 cup orange juice

Mint (optional)

Directions

Simply combine all ingredients into a blender, and puree on high speed. Serve immediately and enjoy a cold, sweet drink full of nutrients. Top with a mint leaf.

3 Fruit Detox Water

YIELD *1 Drink* | **ACTIVE TIME** *3 Min* | **TOTAL TIME** *15 Min*

Ingredients

2 cups water (or sparkling water)

2 cucumber sliced

2 lime slices

2 grapefruit slices

Sprig of rosemary

Directions

Combine water, cucumber, lime, grapefruit, and rosemary in a glass. Let soak for up to 15 minutes for the flavors to set in.

Lemon and Mint Detox Water

4

YIELD *1 Drink* | **ACTIVE TIME** *3 Min* | **TOTAL TIME** *15 Min*

Ingredients

2 lemon slices

1 tablespoon of lemon juice

Handful of mint

1 cup of water (or sparkling water)

Directions

Combine lemon slices, lemon juice and mint to a glass and fill with water. Let mixture stand in the fridge for 15 minutes for a stronger flavor.

Sugar-Free Lemonade with Fresh Blueberries and Herbs

5

YIELD *4 Drinks* | **ACTIVE TIME** *3 Min* | **TOTAL TIME** *15 Min*

Ingredients

1 ½ cups lemon juice

½ cup honey

6 cups water

1 cup blueberries

1/4 cup mixed fresh herbs, such as basil, mint or tarragon

1 cup sparkling water

Directions

Pour lemon juice into a pitcher and combine with honey until dissolved. Add water and stir well. Mash blueberries and herbs in a bowl with a wooden spoon. Add to cup and pour lemonade on top.

6 Date Horchata

YIELD 6 Servings | **ACTIVE TIME** 5 Min | **TOTAL TIME** 5 Min

Ingredients

6 cups water

1 cup rice

½ cup dates

1 ½ teaspoons vanilla extract

3 tablespoons cinnamon

1 tablespoon maple syrup (optional)

1 cup almond milk

Directions

Heat up 2 cups of water until bubbles start appearing but not quite at a boil. Remove from heat and add in rice. Cover and soak for 2 hours until rice is soft but is still slightly raw. Drain water and add rice to a food processor or blender. Add in the remaining 4 cups of water, dates, vanilla, and cinnamon. Blend until smooth, about 1 minute. Taste for sweetness, add more dates or maple syrup as desired.

Strain rice mixture into a bowl through a fine strainer or cheesecloth, whisk in almond milk. Discard any rice chunks that remain. Transfer milk mixture into a pitcher with a lid. Serve over ice.

7 Red Wine

Directions

In this diet, we don't shy away from an occasional drink. The go to is red wine due to its heart benefits and the moderate amount of the antioxidant flavonoids. You only get these benefits with red, unfortunately. Don't substitute margaritas or sangria because they are both high in added sugar.

Remember that red wine is only healthy as part of an overall healthy lifestyle. It's important to limit yourself to 1 glass a day. If you don't enjoy wine, there's no need to start drinking it.

Mediterranean
~ Dessert ~

Dessert

1) *Frozen Blueberry Yogurt
   Swirl Pop Cups*   *58*

2) *Frozen Bananas*   *59*

3) *Chocolate Chia Pudding
   with Raspberries*   *60*

4) *Chia seed and Mango Puree
   with Blueberries*   *61*

5) *Caramelized Pear with Gorgonzola*   *62*

6) *Natural Caramel Sauce*   *63*

7) *Chocolate Cookies*   *64*

8) *Pistachio Pudding*   *65*

Frozen Blueberry Yogurt Swirl Pop Cups

1

YIELD *8 Popsicles* | **ACTIVE TIME** *5 Min* | **TOTAL TIME** *8 Hours*

Ingredients

2 cups blueberries

2 tablespoons honey

2 cups Greek yogurt

8 wooden craft sticks

Directions

Puree the blueberries in a food processor or blender. Pour into a bowl and add the honey. Gently mix in the yogurt. Pour mixture into a popsicle mold and insert wooden craft sticks. Freeze overnight and run under warm water to get the popsicle out of the mold. Feel free to experiment with other berries and fruit.

② Frozen Bananas

YIELD *16 Popsicles* | **ACTIVE TIME** *20 Min* | **TOTAL TIME** *5 Hours*

Ingredients

4 bananas, quartered

1/3 cup almond butter

¼ cup dark chocolate

½ cup chopped almond (or cashews, or walnuts)

16 wooden craft sticks

Directions

Cut the bananas into small 2 or 3-inch-long segments. Gently stick the wooden craft sticks into the bottom of each chunk. Freeze the bananas on a tray for about 3 hours. Remove bananas from freezer and coat with almond butter. Freeze for another hour. Melt the chocolate over a double boiler and dip each banana piece into the chocolate. Lightly roll over chopped almonds and set aside to dry.

Chocolate Chia Pudding with Raspberries

3

YIELD *2 Servings* | **ACTIVE TIME** *15 Min* | **TOTAL TIME** *8 Hours*

Ingredients

1 ½ cups almond milk

¼ cup dark chocolate

¼ cup chia seeds

¼ cup raspberries

¼ cup almonds, slived

Mint leaves

Directions

Add 1 cup of almond milk to a pot and add dark chocolate. Over low heat, slowly melt the chocolate. Slowly add the remaining milk while stirring. Remove from heat and cool to room temperature. Pour into a container and mix in chia seeds. Mix well. Let stand for 15 minutes before mixing again. Leave the container covered in a refrigerator over night. Stir the chia seed mixture with a fork and add raspberries, almonds, and mint leaves as garnish.

Chia Seed and Mango Puree with Blueberries

4

YIELD *2 Servings* | **ACTIVE TIME** *15 Min* | **TOTAL TIME** *2 ½ hours*

Ingredients

¼ cup chia seeds

1 ½ cups almond milk

1 tablespoon honey

½ teaspoon vanilla extract

1 mango

½ cup blueberries

Mint leaf (optional)

Directions

Mix the chia seeds, milk, honey, vanilla extract in a bowl until combined. Allow the chia seed mixture to rest for 2 hours until gel-like. Puree the mango in a food processor or blender. Mix mango puree into the chia seed mixture. Top with blueberries and mint.

5 Caramelized Pear with Gorgonzola

YIELD *2 Servings* | **ACTIVE TIME** *20 Min* | **TOTAL TIME** *45 Min*

Ingredients

2 tablespoons olive oil

1 ripe pear, peeled

¼ cup gorgonzola cheese

3 tablespoons honey

¼ cup natural caramel sauce

Directions

Heat olive oil in pan over medium heat. Add the pear, sliced in half. Cook until golden brown. Remove from heat and slice the pears into small strips. Add the pears back to the pan over low heat and add the gorgonzola cheese. Continue until the cheese begins to melt. Serve on a plate and top with caramel sauce.

6 Natural Caramel Sauce

YIELD *1 Jar* | **ACTIVE TIME** *20 Min* | **TOTAL TIME** *20 Min*

Ingredients

¼ cup water

6 tablespoons powdered erythritol

2 tablespoons maple syrup

¼ cup butter

¾ cup heavy cream

Directions

In a pot mix the water, erythritol and syrup. Simmer on medium heat until the water starts to boil. Add the butter and whisk for about 10 minutes until the mixture begins to brown. Add in the cream and whisk for 2 minutes. Once the sauce begins to thicken and gets the consistency of carmel sauce, turn off the heat. Feel free to serve immediately or store in a jar for up to 2 weeks.

7 Chocolate Cookies

YIELD *2 DOZEN* | **ACTIVE TIME** *20 Min* | **TOTAL TIME** *30 Min*

Ingredients

1 cup olive oil

1 tablespoon vanilla extract

2 ½ cups honey

1 teaspoon salt

1 large egg

2 cups whole-wheat flour

½ teaspoon baking soda

2 cups dark chocolate chips

Directions

Preheat oven to 350F and prepare two baking sheets with parchment paper. Combine the oil, vanilla, honey, and salt in a large bowl until smooth. Mix in the egg. In a separate bowl, combine flour and baking soda. Combine wet and dry ingredients. Fold in chocolate chips. Form dough into 1-inch balls and then slightly press onto baking sheet, leaving room for cookie to expand. Bake until cookies are golden brown around the edges, about 10 minutes. Cool on a rack, serve.

8   Pistachio Pudding

YIELD *6 Servings* | **ACTIVE TIME** *30 Min* | **TOTAL TIME** *5 Hours*

Ingredients

1 cup pistachios, unsalted and shelled

½ cup honey

2 cups + 2 tablespoons almond milk

3 eggs

2 tablespoons maple syrup

Pinch of salt

2 tablespoon olive oil

¼ tablespoon vanilla extract

Directions

Blend the pistachios in a food processor or blender until finely ground. Add ¼ cup of honey and 2 tablespoons of the almond milk. Pulse until a smooth paste forms. In a deep saucepan, combine the pistachio mixture and remaining 2 cups of almond milk. Cook over medium-high heat until the mixture begins to steam. In a food processor or blender, add in the remaining honey, 1 whole egg, 2 egg yolks, maple syrup and salt. Slowly add ½ cup of the warm milk mixture to the food processor or blender.

Slowly add the contents of the food processor or blender into the saucepan and continue to cook. Reduce the heat to medium and stir frequently until the pudding begins to thicken. Remove from heat before stirring in the oil and vanilla. Divide into 6 serving cups, and chill for 4 hours. Serve cold with chopped pistachios as garnish.

Mediterranean
Snacks

Snacks

1 *Easy Tahini Sauce*

YIELD *1 1/4 cups* | **ACTIVE TIME** *20 Min* | **TOTAL TIME** *20 Min*

Ingredients

2 garlic cloves, minced

½ teaspoon salt

½ cup well-stirred tahini

1/3 cup lemon juice

¼ cup water

¼ cup olive oil

¼ teaspoon cumin

1 teaspoon cilantro

1 teaspoon parsley

Directions

Whisk together garlic, salt, tahini, lemon juice, water, olive oil, and cumin. Garnish with parsley and cilantro. Serve at room temperature.

② Homemade Tahini Sauce

YIELD *1 ¹/₄ cups* | **ACTIVE TIME** *20 Min* | **TOTAL TIME** *20 Min*

Ingredients

½ cup hulled sesame seeds

2-4 tablespoons of olive oil

Pinch of salt (optional)

Directions

Grind sesame seeds with olive oil in a food processor or blender until smooth.

For a more nutty flavor, try lightly toasting the sesame seeds on a stovetop before blending - *don't use an oven because sesame seeds burn easily.*

3 Creamy Tahini Hummus

| YIELD *3 cups* | ACTIVE TIME *20 Min* | TOTAL TIME *20 Min* |

Ingredients

¼ cup lemon juice

¼ cup tahini

2 tablespoons olive oil

1 garlic clove

½ teaspoon cumin

½ teaspoon salt

1 ½ cups of canned chickpeas

2-3 tablespoons water (optional)

Dash of paprika

Fresh veggies

Directions

In a food processor or blender– combine the tahini and lemon juice. Slowly add the olive oil, garlic, cumin, and salt. Add the rinsed chickpeas. Add water if the mixture is too thick. Continue to blend until smooth. Serve topped with paprika and use veggies to dip!

4 Beetroot Hummus

YIELD *2 ½ cups* | **ACTIVE TIME** *10 Min* | **TOTAL TIME** *50 Min*

Ingredients

1 beet

2 cloves garlic, peeled

2 tablespoons olive oil

1 ½ cups cooked chickpeas, drained and rinsed or from a can

2 tablespoons tahini (see our recipe, or get store made)

2 tablespoons lemon juice

3 tablespoons warm water

½ teaspoon cumin (optional)

½ teaspoon coriander (optional)

Dash of sea salt and black pepper

Directions

Preheat your oven to 400F. Wrap the beet in foil with the garlic and olive oil. On a baking sheet, roast for 30 minutes or until the beet is fork-tender. Leave out to cool... then remove the beet skin. Place the beet in a food processor and blend while adding the rest of the ingredients. Keep in the fridge until ready to use. Serve with veggies!

5 Mediterranean Hummus Stuffed Peppers

YIELD 6 Servings | **ACTIVE TIME** 10 Min | **TOTAL TIME** 30 Min

Ingredients

3 bell peppers

½ cup of hummus

½ cup olives , sliced

½ cup feta cheese

2 tablespoons parsley

Directions

Preheat the oven to 400F. Cut the top of the bell peppers and remove seeds. Place the whole peppers on a sheet pan and place in the oven for 30-40 minutes, until the skins are wrinkled and the peppers are soften, turning them twice while roasting. Put a scoop of hummus in each and garnish with chopped olives, feta cheese and a sprinkle of parsley.

This is the perfect snack to bring to a party!

6 *A piece of fruit*

Directions

Don't under estimate the hunger satisfying power of a piece of fruit. A perfect source of healthy sugar, it'll help curb your sweet tooth. And because fruit is full of fiber, they are less likely to spike your blood sugar levels. So, go ahead and grab an apple, an orange, or even a handful of berries!

Fruit is often overlooked when considering a snack. But in the Mediterranean Diet, it's important to get your sugar from healthy sources… and none are better than a perfect piece of fruit.

7 Nuts

Ingredients

Unsalted almonds

Walnuts and cashews

Directions

Almonds are highly nutritious and rich in healthy fats, antioxidants, vitamins and minerals. Walnuts have omega-3, iron, selenium, calcium, zinc, vitamin E and even some B vitamins! Combined with cashews, this quick snack helps heart health and reduces risks of blood disease. So go ahead and grab a handful whenever hunger strikes!

8 Chickpea Salad

YIELD *2 Servings* | **ACTIVE TIME** *15 Min* | **TOTAL TIME** *15 Min*

Ingredients

Salad
1 can chickpeas
½ cup sundried tomatoes
½ cup cucumber, chopped
½ red onion, sliced
½ cup of olives, sliced
¼ cup parsley
¼ cup feta

Dressing
¼ cup of olive oil
2 tablespoons red wine vinegar
½ teaspoon cumin
Salt and pepper to taste

Directions

Drain the can of chickpeas and combine with sundried tomatoes, cucumbers, onion and olives. Top with parsley and feta.

In a separate bowl, combine the dressing ingredients. Refrigerate both for an hour before combining and serving.

9 Apple Slices with Almond Butter

YIELD *1 Serving* | **ACTIVE TIME** *10 Min* | **TOTAL TIME** *10 Min*

Ingredients

1 apple
½ cup almond butter
2 tablespoons almonds, sliced
2 tablespoons walnuts, crushed
2 tablespoons dark chocolate chips

Directions

Core and slice the apple into thin strips. Spread almond butter over apple slices and top with sliced almonds, walnut chunks and dark chocolate chips.

10 Chili Lime Roasted Chickpeas

YIELD 2 ½ cups | **ACTIVE TIME** 10 Min | **TOTAL TIME** 45 Min

Ingredients

1 can chickpeas, rinsed, drained and dried

2 tablespoons olive oil

1 teaspoon chili powder

½ teaspoon cumin

1 lime zested

¼ teaspoon garlic powder

¼ teaspoon salt

Directions

Preheat oven to 400F.

Place the chickpeas on a rimmed baking sheet in a single layer. Drizzle chickpeas with olive oil. Stir with a wooden spoon. Bake for 30-40 minutes, until lightly browned. Remove from oven.

Mix remaining ingredients together and sprinkle over the chickpeas. Serve warm or store in an airtight container up to 3 days.

Chickpeas are so versatile in the Mediterranean Diet – you'll never have too many Chickpeas in your pantry going unused. They can be used in all sorts of recipes and are an amazing source of protein and fiber. A very healthy source of carbohydrates. They contain several essential vitamins and minerals.

11

Plain Greek Yogurt and Fresh Berries

| YIELD *1 Serving* | ACTIVE TIME *10 Min* | TOTAL TIME *10 Min* |

Ingredients

1 cup Greek yogurt

½ cup blueberries (or strawberries, or raspberries

Mint (optional)

1 cup oatmeal (optional)

Directions

Simply combine yogurt and berries for a delicious snack. Add in some cooked oatmeal to transform into a full breakfast!